Silver Burdett Ginn
Mathematics

Practice Workbook

Cumulative Practice

Mixed Review

2

Silver Burdett Ginn
Parsippany, NJ • Needham, MA
Atlanta, GA • Deerfield, IL • Irving, TX • Santa Clara, CA

Silver Burdett Ginn
A Division of Simon & Schuster
299 Jefferson Road, P.O. Box 480
Parsippany, NJ 07054-0480

ISBN 0-382-37289-1

3 4 5 6 7 8 9-B-00 99 98

Contents

Contents

Name _____

Using Order in Addition

Count. Write how many in all.

1.
$$3 + 2 = 5$$ (baseballs: 3 + 2, total 5)

$$2 + 3$$ (baseballs: 2 + 3)

$$\begin{array}{r} 2 \\ +3 \\ \hline \end{array} \qquad \begin{array}{r} 3 \\ +2 \\ \hline \end{array}$$

2.
$$\begin{array}{r} 6 \\ +1 \\ \hline \end{array} \qquad \begin{array}{r} 1 \\ +6 \\ \hline \end{array} \qquad \begin{array}{r} 6 \\ +1 \\ \hline \end{array} \qquad \begin{array}{r} 1 \\ +6 \\ \hline \end{array}$$

3.
$$3 + 2 = \underline{\qquad} \qquad 6 + 2 = \underline{\qquad} \qquad 3 + 7 = \underline{\qquad}$$

$$2 + 3 = \underline{\qquad} \qquad 2 + 6 = \underline{\qquad} \qquad 7 + 3 = \underline{\qquad}$$

4.
$$1 + 8 = \underline{\qquad} \qquad 5 + 6 = \underline{\qquad} \qquad 2 + 9 = \underline{\qquad}$$

$$8 + 1 = \underline{\qquad} \qquad 6 + 5 = \underline{\qquad} \qquad 9 + 2 = \underline{\qquad}$$

Review and Remember

Write the number.

1. two _____   ten _____   six _____   nine _____

Draw more hats to make the number.

2. 5

Using Doubles to Add

Write the addend to make a double.
Find each sum.

1.
$$3 \atop +3 \atop \overline{6}$$
  $$4 \atop +\underline{}$$
  $$2 \atop +\underline{}$$
  $$0 \atop +\underline{}$$
  $$5 \atop +\underline{}$$
  $$6 \atop +\underline{}$$

Circle doubles. Add.

2.
$$3 \atop +4$$
  $$1 \atop +1$$
  $$2 \atop +1$$
  $$3 \atop +7$$
  $$1 \atop +9$$
  $$2 \atop +6$$

3.
$$4 \atop +4$$
  $$3 \atop +3$$
  $$3 \atop +6$$
  $$2 \atop +9$$
  $$2 \atop +2$$
  $$0 \atop +1$$

4.
$$3 \atop +8$$
  $$0 \atop +0$$
  $$9 \atop +1$$
  $$2 \atop +7$$
  $$1 \atop +6$$
  $$3 \atop +9$$

Review and Remember

Write two number sentences for each picture.

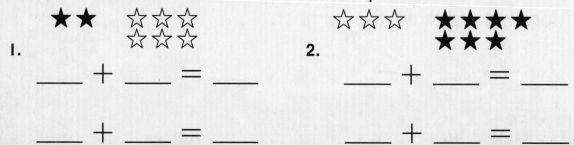

1. ___ + ___ = ___

   ___ + ___ = ___

2. ___ + ___ = ___

   ___ + ___ = ___

Name _____

Three Addends

Add.

1.
$$\begin{array}{r} 5 \\ 1 \\ +4 \\ \hline 10 \end{array}\quad>\quad \begin{array}{r} 6 \\ \\ +4 \\ \hline 10 \end{array}\qquad\qquad \begin{array}{r} 5 \\ 1 \\ +4 \\ \hline \end{array}\quad>\quad \begin{array}{r} 5 \\ \\ +5 \\ \hline \end{array}$$

2.
$$\begin{array}{r} 3 \\ 1 \\ +3 \\ \hline \end{array}\qquad \begin{array}{r} 7 \\ 0 \\ +4 \\ \hline \end{array}\qquad \begin{array}{r} 3 \\ 3 \\ +3 \\ \hline \end{array}\qquad \begin{array}{r} 5 \\ 2 \\ +3 \\ \hline \end{array}\qquad \begin{array}{r} 1 \\ 4 \\ +1 \\ \hline \end{array}$$

3.
$$\begin{array}{r} 0 \\ 4 \\ +5 \\ \hline \end{array}\qquad \begin{array}{r} 3 \\ 2 \\ +6 \\ \hline \end{array}\qquad \begin{array}{r} 6 \\ 3 \\ +3 \\ \hline \end{array}\qquad \begin{array}{r} 4 \\ 2 \\ +3 \\ \hline \end{array}\qquad \begin{array}{r} 4 \\ 4 \\ +4 \\ \hline \end{array}$$

4. $4 + 2 + 1 = \underline{\quad}$ $6 + 2 + 2 = \underline{\quad}$

5. $9 + 0 + 2 = \underline{\quad}$ $6 + 2 + 4 = \underline{\quad}$

Review and Remember

1. Circle the greater number.

6	8		4	1

2. Write the number.

seven _____   two _____

Counting Back

Subtract. Count back. Use the number line if you like.

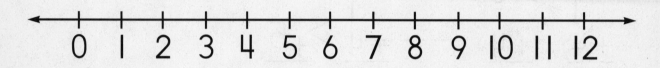

1. $5 - 2 =$ ___3___ $6 - 3 =$ _____ $4 - 1 =$ _____

2. $7 - 2 =$ _____ $12 - 2 =$ _____ $11 - 1 =$ _____

3. $7 - 3 =$ _____ $11 - 2 =$ _____ $12 - 1 =$ _____

4.
$$\begin{array}{r} 10 \\ -2 \\ \hline \end{array} \qquad \begin{array}{r} 7 \\ -3 \\ \hline \end{array} \qquad \begin{array}{r} 11 \\ -3 \\ \hline \end{array} \qquad \begin{array}{r} 6 \\ -2 \\ \hline \end{array} \qquad \begin{array}{r} 9 \\ -1 \\ \hline \end{array}$$

5.
$$\begin{array}{r} 12 \\ -3 \\ \hline \end{array} \qquad \begin{array}{r} 11 \\ -0 \\ \hline \end{array} \qquad \begin{array}{r} 8 \\ -2 \\ \hline \end{array} \qquad \begin{array}{r} 5 \\ -3 \\ \hline \end{array} \qquad \begin{array}{r} 9 \\ -3 \\ \hline \end{array}$$

Review and Remember

Add or subtract.

$$\begin{array}{r} 8 \\ +2 \\ \hline \end{array} \qquad \begin{array}{r} 6 \\ -3 \\ \hline \end{array} \qquad \begin{array}{r} 9 \\ +1 \\ \hline \end{array} \qquad \begin{array}{r} 8 \\ -4 \\ \hline \end{array} \qquad \begin{array}{r} 7 \\ +1 \\ \hline \end{array} \qquad \begin{array}{r} 4 \\ +5 \\ \hline \end{array}$$

Name _____

Related Addition and Subtraction

Write an addition fact.
Then write a related subtraction fact.

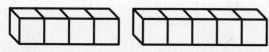

1. $\underline{4} + \underline{5} = \underline{9}$ $\qquad$ $\underline{9} - \underline{5} = \underline{4}$

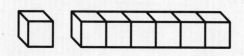

2. ___ + ___ = ___ $\qquad$ ___ − ___ = ___

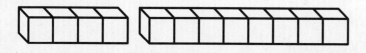

3. ___ + ___ = ___ $\qquad$ ___ − ___ = ___

Add or subtract.

4.
$\begin{array}{c} 10 \\ -6 \\ \hline \end{array}$
$\begin{array}{c} 4 \\ +6 \\ \hline \end{array}$
$\begin{array}{c} 11 \\ -5 \\ \hline \end{array}$
$\begin{array}{c} 6 \\ +5 \\ \hline \end{array}$
$\begin{array}{c} 3 \\ +5 \\ \hline \end{array}$
$\begin{array}{c} 8 \\ -5 \\ \hline \end{array}$

Review and Remember

What double facts are missing?
Complete each fact.

1. ___ + ___ = 4 $\qquad$ ___ + ___ = 10 $\qquad$ ___ + ___ = 6

2. ___ + ___ = 2 $\qquad$ ___ + ___ = 12 $\qquad$ ___ + ___ = 8

$\qquad$

Name _____

Make a Graph

The pictograph shows how
many pets the children in
Mrs. Hope's class have.

Cats	🐱	🐱	🐱	🐱		
Dogs	🐕	🐕	🐕	🐕	🐕	

0 1 2 3 4 5 6

1. How many cats do the children have?   ____

2. How many dogs do the children have?   ____

Make a bar graph to show the total numbers.
Sarah had 1 stone and 4 acorns.
Jimmy had 3 stones and 2 acorns.

3. How many spaces do you color
   for Sarah and Jimmy's stones?
   Color them.   ____

4. How many spaces do you color
   for Sarah and Jimmy's acorns?
   Color them.   ____

Review and Remember

Add or subtract.

$$3 + 0 \qquad 0 + 10 \qquad 6 - 2 \qquad 14 - 7 \qquad 8 - 7$$

Fact Families to 18

Subtract.
Circle the related addition fact.

1.
$$13$$
$$-4$$

$5 + 9 = 14$
$4 + 8 = 12$
$9 + 4 = 13$

2.
$$14$$
$$-6$$

$6 + 9 = 15$
$6 + 8 = 14$
$6 + 7 = 13$

Add or subtract.

3.
$$15$$
$$-6$$

$$3$$
$$+7$$

$$16$$
$$-9$$

$$14$$
$$-7$$

$$7$$
$$+8$$

$$3$$
$$+8$$

Circle names for 10.

4. $7 + 3$ $5 + 6$ $12 - 2$ $16 - 6$

Review and Remember

Add or subtract.

1.
$$12$$
$$-5$$

$$11$$
$$-8$$

$$4$$
$$+8$$

$$6$$
$$+6$$

$$10$$
$$-4$$

$$8$$
$$+7$$

2. $9 - 6 = \underline{\quad}$ $10 - 8 = \underline{\quad}$ $1 + 6 = \underline{\quad}$

Name _____

Identifying Names for Numbers

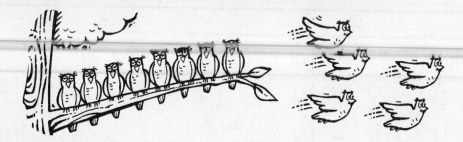

Look at the picture.

1. Write two addition facts.   2. Write two subtraction facts.

___ + ___ = ___   ___ − ___ = ___

___ + ___ = ___   ___ − ___ = ___

Circle names for each number.

3. 7   1 + 6   14 − 7   5 + 3   16 − 9

4. 9   18 − 9   9 + 0   15 − 6   13 − 4

Write four names for 5.

5.

_____ _____ _____ _____

Review and Remember

Solve.

$$\begin{array}{c} 11 \\ -4 \\ \hline \end{array} \qquad \begin{array}{c} 3 \\ +4 \\ \hline \end{array} \qquad \begin{array}{c} 0 \\ +7 \\ \hline \end{array} \qquad \begin{array}{c} 7 \\ +9 \\ \hline \end{array} \qquad \begin{array}{c} 15 \\ -6 \\ \hline \end{array} \qquad \begin{array}{c} 16 \\ -7 \\ \hline \end{array}$$

Name _____

Exploring Regrouping

Draw tens and ones models to show each number.

1. | Show 16 ones | Regroup 16 ones.
Make a group of 10.
Show 1 ten and 6 ones. |
   |---|---|
   | | |

Show each number. Regroup when you can.

2. 16 ones   ____ ten   ____ ones

3. 14 ones   ____ ten   ____ ones

4. 1 ten 10 ones   ____ tens   ____ ones

5. 1 ten 16 ones   ____ tens   ____ ones

6. 1 ten 19 ones   ____ tens   ____ ones

7. 2 tens 19 ones   ____ tens   ____ ones

8. 5 tens 12 ones   ____ tens   ____ ones

Review and Remember

Find the correct name. Fill in the ◯.

1. 16
   ◯ 1 + 6
   ◯ 7 + 7
   ◯ 9 + 7

2. 9
   ◯ 14 − 6
   ◯ 13 − 4
   ◯ 17 − 9

3. 8
   ◯ 4 + 5
   ◯ 9 − 2
   ◯ 16 − 8

4. 15
   ◯ 8 + 7
   ◯ 1 + 5
   ◯ 6 + 8

Use after Grade 2, text page 80.   **11**

Name _____

Skip Counting and Patterns

Skip count.
Write the numbers as you count.

1. __5__ , __10__ , ___ , ___ , ___ , ___ , ___ , ___

2. __3__ , __6__ , ___ , ___ , ___ , ___ , ___ , ___

3. __10__ , __20__ , ___ , ___ , ___ , ___ , ___ , ___

Look for the pattern.
Then write the missing numbers.

4. __12__ , ___ , __16__ , ___ , __20__ , ___ , ___ , ___

5. __3__ , __6__ , ___ , ___ , __15__ , __18__ , ___ , ___

6. ___ , __10__ , __15__ , ___ , __25__ , ___ , ___ , ___

7. ___ , ___ , __50__ , __60__ , __70__ , ___ , ___ , ___

Review and Remember

Circle the odd numbers.

1. 2   5   47   56   99

Circle the even numbers.

2. 4   18   21   72   89

3. If a number ends in 0, is it odd or even?

_____

Name _____

Numbers to 99

Circle the number that is greater.

1. | 18   17 | | 57   71 | | 33   113 |

Circle the number that is less.

2. | 80   79 | | 22   9 | | 98   99 |

Compare. Write the numbers to make each sentence true.

3.   14   21   14   21

_____ is greater than _____.   _____ is less than _____.

____ > ____   ____ < ____

Write > or < in each ◯.

4.   85 ◯ 10   20 ◯ 40   30 ◯ 29   89 ◯ 98

Review and Remember

Add or subtract.

1. $12 - 7 =$ _____ $18 - 9 =$ _____ $14 - 6 =$ _____

2. $9 + 6 =$ _____ $4 + 9 =$ _____ $4 - 4 =$ _____

Name _____

Ordering Numbers

Write the number that comes **after**.

1. 18, _19_   23, ____   44, ____   12, ____

2. 63, ____   94, ____   39, ____   57, ____

Write the number that comes **before**.

3. ____,61   ____,47   ____,79   ____,53

4. ____,82   ____,15   ____,21   ____,38

Write the number that comes **between**.

5. 93, ____,95   87, ____, 89   40, ____,42

6. 10, ____, 12   68, ____, 70   55, ____,57

Review and Remember

Add or subtract.

$$
\begin{array}{cccccc}
4 & 11 & 8 & 3 & 5 & 6 \\
+0 & -7 & -4 & +8 & -5 & +6 \\
\hline
\end{array}
$$

Name _____

Ordinal Numbers

first second third fourth fifth sixth seventh eighth ninth tenth

1st   2nd   3rd   4th   5th   6th   7th   8th   9th   10th

Circle the place where each student is found.

1.

first
third
fifth

ninth
seventh
eighth

second
third
fourth

2.

sixth
fifth
seventh

third
second
first

tenth
twelfth
ninth

Write the number and the word.

3.

_____ _____

Review and Remember

Write the number.

3 tens 8 ones _____   8 tens 3 ones _____

Name _____

Counting Sets of Coins

Count the money. Write the amount.

1.

__25__ ¢   __30__ ¢   _____ ¢   _____ ¢

2.

_____ ¢   _____ ¢   _____ ¢   _____ ¢

Circle the coins you need.

3.

 38¢

Review and Remember

Circle the odd numbers.

1. 25 , 14, 36, 99 , 27 , 43 , 8, 71 ,   1

Write the number.

2. 2 tens 7 ones _____   7 tens 2 ones _____

Name _____

Ways to Show Amounts

Match the amounts of money.
Write each amount. Then draw a line.

1.  _____

a.  _____

2.  _____

b.  _____

3.  _____

c.  _____

Review and Remember

Jessie read 3 books about bears.
She read 8 books about dinosaurs.
How many books did Jessie read?   _____ books

Name _____

Exploring Dollars

Write how many coins there are.
Write each amount.

1.

__20__ nickels = $ __1.00__

2.

____ dimes = $ _____

3.

____ quarters = $ _____

4.

____ half dollars = $ _____

Review and Remember

Write the missing addends that give each sum.

1.
┌──────┐
│ 17 │
└──────┘

__9__ + __8__

____ + __9__

2.
┌──────┐
│ 16 │
└──────┘

____ + __9__

____ + __7__

__8__ + ____

3.
┌──────┐
│ 15 │
└──────┘

____ + __7__

____ + __8__

__9__ + ____

__6__ + ____

Name _____

Using Data From a Picture

Find how many in all.

1. 🐢 _6_ + 🐱 _4_ = ___

2. 🐟 ___ + 🦜 ___ = ___

3. 🐱 ___ + 🐶 ___ = ___

4. 🐱 ___ + 🐢 ___ = ___

5. 🐹 ___ + 🐢 ___ = ___

Review and Remember

Add or subtract.

1.
$$
\begin{array}{r} 12 \\ +5 \\ \hline \end{array}
\qquad
\begin{array}{r} 8 \\ -7 \\ \hline \end{array}
\qquad
\begin{array}{r} 11 \\ -6 \\ \hline \end{array}
\qquad
\begin{array}{r} 6 \\ +6 \\ \hline \end{array}
\qquad
\begin{array}{r} 14 \\ -8 \\ \hline \end{array}
$$

2. $1 + 2 + 7 =$ ___ $\qquad$ $4 + 7 + 1 =$ ___

Use after Grade 2, text page 124. **19**

Name _____

Making Change

Count up from the price. Write the change.

	You pay	Price	Count up	Change
1.	40¢	29¢	_30_ ¢ ____ ¢	_11_ ¢
2.	70¢	57¢	_58_ ¢ ____ ¢ ____ ¢ ____ ¢	____ ¢
3.	50¢	23¢	____ ¢ ____ ¢ ____ ¢	____ ¢

Review and Remember

Write the missing numbers.

1. 2, 4, ____, ____, 10, 12, ____, ____

2. 3, 6, 9, ____, ____, ____, 21, ____

Getting Data From a Table

Use the table to answer each question.

1. Are there more boys or girls in the class?

   _____

Class Birthdays		
Season	Boys	Girls
Spring	1	2
Summer	3	5
Fall	5	0
Winter	3	4

2. What time of the year do most students have birthdays?

   _____

3. What time of the year do the fewest students have birthdays?

   _____

5. How many girls are in the class?

   _____

4. How many boys are in the class?

   _____

6. How many students are in the class?

   _____

7. When is your birthday?

   _____

Review and Remember

Add.

$$\begin{array}{c}8\\+9\\\hline\end{array} \qquad \begin{array}{c}5\\+5\\\hline\end{array} \qquad \begin{array}{c}6\\+7\\\hline\end{array} \qquad \begin{array}{c}9\\+5\\\hline\end{array} \qquad \begin{array}{c}8\\+5\\\hline\end{array} \qquad \begin{array}{c}7\\+9\\\hline\end{array} \qquad \begin{array}{c}1\\+9\\\hline\end{array}$$

Name _____

Deciding When to Regroup

Use tens and ones models.
Complete the chart.

	Do you need to regroup?	How many are left?
1. Show 1 ten and 5 ones. Subtract 3 ones.	yes (no)	_1_ ten _2_ ones
2. Show 3 tens and 9 ones. Subtract 6 ones.	yes no	___ tens ___ ones
3. Show 8 tens and 4 ones. Subtract 5 ones.	yes no	___ tens ___ ones
4. Show 1 ten and 1 one. Subtract 6 ones.	yes no	___ tens ___ ones
5. Show 6 tens and 7 ones. Subtract 3 ones.	yes no	___ tens ___ ones

Review and Remember

Estimate.

Today 18 planes fly from New York to
Boston. Then 11 planes fly from Atlanta
to Boston. About how many planes fly
from New York and Atlanta to Boston?

about _____ planes

Name _____

Adding and Subtracting Money

Add or subtract. Regroup if you need to.

1. $\begin{array}{r} 48¢ \\ -9¢ \\ \hline \end{array}$ $\begin{array}{r} 63¢ \\ +36¢ \\ \hline \end{array}$ $\begin{array}{r} 44¢ \\ -44¢ \\ \hline \end{array}$ $\begin{array}{r} 71¢ \\ -17¢ \\ \hline \end{array}$

2. $\begin{array}{r} 57¢ \\ +38¢ \\ \hline \end{array}$ $\begin{array}{r} 57¢ \\ -48¢ \\ \hline \end{array}$ $\begin{array}{r} 98¢ \\ -69¢ \\ \hline \end{array}$ $\begin{array}{r} 34¢ \\ +17¢ \\ \hline \end{array}$

3. $\begin{array}{r} 25¢ \\ +15¢ \\ \hline \end{array}$ $\begin{array}{r} 30¢ \\ -15¢ \\ \hline \end{array}$ $\begin{array}{r} 35¢ \\ +30¢ \\ \hline \end{array}$ $\begin{array}{r} 55¢ \\ -5¢ \\ \hline \end{array}$

4. $\begin{array}{r} 85¢ \\ -59¢ \\ \hline \end{array}$ $\begin{array}{r} 93¢ \\ -26¢ \\ \hline \end{array}$ $\begin{array}{r} 54¢ \\ +45¢ \\ \hline \end{array}$ $\begin{array}{r} 83¢ \\ -38¢ \\ \hline \end{array}$

Review and Remember

Add.

$\begin{array}{r} 43 \\ +18 \\ \hline \end{array}$ $\begin{array}{r} 16 \\ +38 \\ \hline \end{array}$ $\begin{array}{r} 74 \\ +12 \\ \hline \end{array}$ $\begin{array}{r} 57 \\ +21 \\ \hline \end{array}$ $\begin{array}{r} 16 \\ +39 \\ \hline \end{array}$

Name _____

Choosing the Operation

There are 23 students in Miss Gonko's
class. Mr. Brisk has 20 students.
How many students are there in all?
Do you add or subtract?
Circle the example that makes sense.

$$\begin{array}{r} 23 \\ +20 \\ \hline 43 \end{array} \qquad \begin{array}{r} 23 \\ -20 \\ \hline 3 \end{array}$$

Write each sum or difference.
Circle the example that makes sense.

1. How many more students does
   Miss Gonko have than Mr. Brisk?

$$\begin{array}{r} 23 \\ -20 \\ \hline \end{array} \qquad \begin{array}{r} 23 \\ +20 \\ \hline \end{array}$$

2. Mrs. Rodgers has 19 students.
   Mr. Wong has 6 more students
   than Mrs. Rodgers. How many
   students are in Mr. Wong's class?

$$\begin{array}{r} 19 \\ +6 \\ \hline \end{array} \qquad \begin{array}{r} 19 \\ -6 \\ \hline \end{array}$$

Review and Remember

Count up to find the change.

1. Monica has 60¢.
   She spends 44¢.

_____ _____ _____ change

2. Barry has 80¢.
   He spends 69¢.

_____ _____ change

Name _____

Pounds

Mr. Lee makes pasta every Thursday.

pasta
1 pound

tomato sauce
3 pounds

Circle the things that are less than 1 pound.
Mark an X on things that are more than 1 pound.

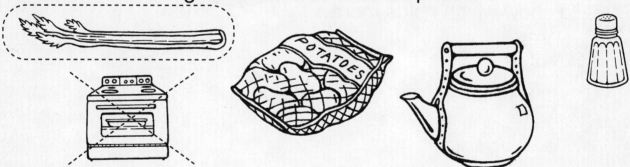

Review and Remember

Add or subtract.

$$\begin{array}{r} 52 \\ -38 \\ \hline \end{array} \qquad \begin{array}{r} 74 \\ +56 \\ \hline \end{array} \qquad \begin{array}{r} 48 \\ -39 \\ \hline \end{array} \qquad \begin{array}{r} 66 \\ -34 \\ \hline \end{array} \qquad \begin{array}{r} 37 \\ -18 \\ \hline \end{array}$$

Name _____

Understanding Capacity

2 cups fill 1 pint   2 pints fill 1 quart

Circle to show the same amount.

1.    2 cups
                            2 pints
                            2 quarts

2.   2 cups
                            2 pints
                            2 quarts

Circle to show which holds more.

3. | 4. | 5.

Solve.

6. Sam bought 2 quarts of fruit juice.
   How many cups can he fill?   _____

Review and Remember

Add or subtract.

$$\begin{array}{cccccc} 9 & 10 & 7 & 6 & 9 & 7 \\ -8 & -7 & +10 & +5 & +4 & -5 \end{array}$$

Name _____

Cups, Pints, and Quarts

2 cups fill 1 pint.   2 pints fill 1 quart.

Circle to show the same amount.

1. 	1 cup 1 pint (1 quart)	2. 	2 cups 2 pints 2 quarts	3.  2 cups 2 pints 2 quarts
4.	1 cup 1 pint 1 quart	5.	1 cup 1 pint 1 quart	6. 2 cups 2 pints 2 quarts

Review and Remember

Estimate. Circle the answer that makes sense.

Two trains pass by. The first has 12 cars. The second
has 19 cars. About how many cars are there?

about 30 cars   about 50 cars   about 70 cars

          Use after Grade 2, text page 242.

Name _____

Temperature

Write each temperature.

Circle the hottest temperature.
Mark an X on the coldest temperature.

1.
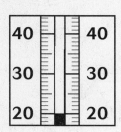

____ F

2.
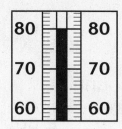

____ F

3.

____ F

Draw a line to match each temperature to a picture.

4. 20°C   5. 40°C   6. 0°C

Review and Remember

Complete the pattern.

⬭ △ ▮ ▢ ⬭ △ ▮ ▢ ____ ____ ____ ____

Name _____

Ordering Numbers to 1,000

Write the numbers in order.

1. 501	502				507			
2.		513						

3. 851				856			
4.		863					
5.						878	
6.			885				

Look at the charts. What patterns do you see?

Review and Remember

Which kitten is Gremlin? Cross out pictures that
do not fit the clues. Circle the
correct picture.

A. Gremlin is not a solid color.

B. Gremlin does not wear bows.

C. Gremlin is sleeping.

 Use after Grade 2, text page 272. **45**

Name _____

Space Shapes and Plane Shapes

Circle three shapes that are the same.

Circle the space shape that could make each plane shape.

Write how many sides and corners.

5. △ A triangle has _____ sides and _____ corners.

6. ☐ A square has _____ sides and _____ corners.

Review and Remember

It is 10:00 in the morning. The game starts in 4 hours.
At what time does the game start? _____
Draw hands to show when the game starts.

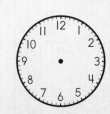

Name _____

Exploring Perimeter

Each is 1 unit. How many units around is each shape?

1.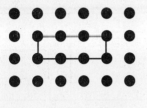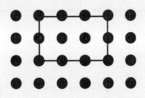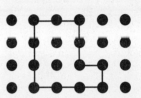

_____ units   _____ units   _____ units

Draw each perimeter.

2. rectangle 6 units around   square 8 units around

3. square 12 units around   rectangle 10 units around

Review and Remember

Count by 100s.

1. 300, _____, 500, 600, _____, _____, _____

Write the number between.

2. 213, _____, 215   499, _____, 501   789, _____, 791

Name _____

Congruent and Symmetric Shapes

Look at the first shape. Circle shapes with the same size and shape.

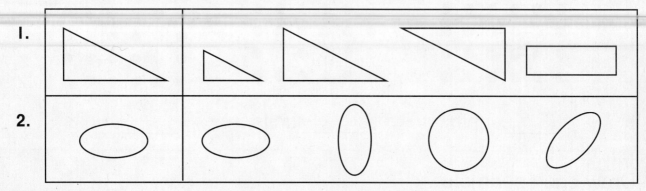

1.

2.

Draw a shape with the same size and shape.

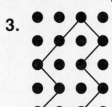

3.

4.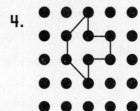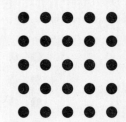

Does each picture have a line of symmetry? Circle **yes** or **no**.

5.

 yes no

 yes no

 yes no

Review and Remember

Write the number.

1. before ____,100   2. after 77,____   3. between 9,____,11

48   Use after Grade 2, text page 297.

© Silver Burdett Ginn Inc.

Understanding Fractions

Write $\frac{1}{2}$, $\frac{1}{3}$, or $\frac{1}{4}$.

1.

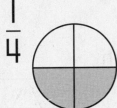 ___ 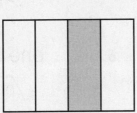 ___ 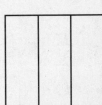 ___

Circle the shape that shows each fraction.

2. $\frac{1}{4}$ 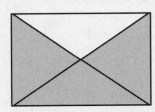 $\frac{1}{3}$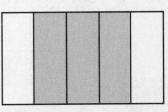

What part is shaded? Fill in the ◯.

3.

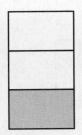   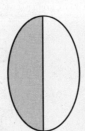   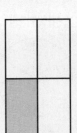

◯ $\frac{1}{4}$ ◯ $\frac{3}{4}$ ◯ $\frac{2}{3}$ ◯ $\frac{1}{3}$ ◯ $\frac{3}{6}$ ◯ $\frac{3}{5}$

Review and Remember

Find the perimeter of each shape.

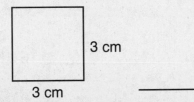 3 cm / 3 cm _____

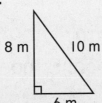 8 m 10 m 6 m _____

Name _____

Working With Fractions

Color to show the fraction.

1. $\frac{2}{6}$ two sixths
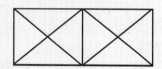

2. $\frac{4}{5}$ four fifths

3. $\frac{7}{8}$ seven eighths

4. $\frac{1}{5}$ one fifth

5. $\frac{5}{6}$ five sixths
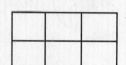

6. $\frac{1}{6}$ one sixth
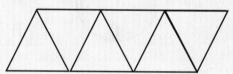

7. $\frac{6}{8}$ six eighths
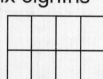

8. $\frac{3}{8}$ three eighths
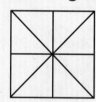

Review and Remember

Read. Cross out the fact that is not needed.
Then solve.

Boat A is 30 feet long.
Boat B is 45 feet long.
Boat B has a crew of 10.
How much longer is boat B than boat A? _____ feet

Name _____

Adding and Subtracting Money

Write the numbers.

1. 6 dollars 9 cents _____

2. $6.93, _____,$6.95, $6.96, _____, _____

Compare. Write > or < in each ◯.

3. $8.98◯$9.89 $2.10◯$2.01 $5.99◯$5.00

Add. Regroup if you need to.

4.
$$\begin{array}{r} \$5.14 \\ + \ 2.06 \\ \hline \end{array} \quad \begin{array}{r} \$4.32 \\ + \ 3.91 \\ \hline \end{array} \quad \begin{array}{r} \$0.21 \\ + \ 0.49 \\ \hline \end{array} \quad \begin{array}{r} \$3.29 \\ + \ 0.91 \\ \hline \end{array} \quad \begin{array}{r} \$0.12 \\ + \ 0.60 \\ \hline \end{array}$$

Review and Remember

Circle the number.

1. 7 hundreds 1 ten 5 ones
   751   715   705

2. 3 hundreds 6 tens 0 ones
   360   306   603

Write the missing numbers.

3. ___,478,479   565,___,567   798,799,___

4. ___,302,303   912,___,914   629,630,___

Name _____

Too Much Information

Which fact is not needed?
Cross it out. Then solve.

1. An Indian elephant has 19 pairs of
   ribs. An elephant's tusks can be 5 feet
   long. An African elephant has 21 pairs
   of ribs. How many more pairs of ribs
   does an African elephant have?   _____ pairs

2. A polar bear ran 35 yards. A cheetah
   ran 35 yards farther. The cheetah had 8
   cubs. How far did the cheetah run?   _____ yards

3. An elephant was 80 years old. Each of
   its tusks weighed about 35 pounds. A
   lion was 25 years old. How much older
   was the elephant than the lion?   _____ years

Review and Remember

Look at the string of beads.
Write a fraction for each kind of bead.

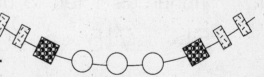

1. ___   2. ___   3. ___
   ___   ___   ___

Name _____

Using Estimation

Think about the underlined words.

Circle the best answer.

1. Which number is <u>about</u> 500?   435 600 502

2. Which number is <u>a bit less</u> than 534?   248 535 529

3. Which number is <u>nearest</u> to 199?   201 113 315

4. Which number is <u>a little more</u> than 579? 499 581 876

Write your own number for each.

5. Write a number that is <u>about</u> 500   _____

6. Write a number that is <u>close</u> to 200   _____

7. Write a number that is <u>a little less</u> than 234.   _____

8. Write a number that is <u>a lot more</u> than 46.   _____

Review and Remember

Solve. Read one clue at a time and cross out. Circle the answer.

Which sweater belongs to Mel?

A. Mel does not wear stripes.

B. Mel's sweater has a picture on it.

C. It does not have a ball on it.

Name _____

Exploring Multiplication

Circle groups of 2. Multiply.

1. 3 groups of 2

$3 \times 2 =$ ____

2. 2 groups of 2

$2 \times 2 =$ ____

3. 4 groups of 2

$4 \times 2 =$ ____

4. 1 group of 2

$1 \times 2 =$ ____

5. 5 groups of 2

$5 \times 2 =$ ____

6. Make your own.

____ $\times$ ____ = ____

Review and Remember

Two classes get on the school bus. There are
21 children in each class. About how many children
get on the bus? Circle the best estimate.

about 20 children   about 30 children   about 40 children

Name _____

Addition and Multiplication

Add. Then multiply.

1. Henry gathers 5 chicken eggs every day.
   How many eggs does he gather in 2 days?

   $5 + 5 =$ _____

   $2 \times 5 =$ _____

2. Teresa writes 3 letters every week.
   How many letters does she write
   in 4 weeks?

   $3 + 3 + 3 + 3 =$ _____

   $4 \times 3 =$ _____

3. Shawn needs 6 flowers for each vase.
   There are 2 vases. How many flowers
   does she need?

   $6 + 6 =$ _____

   $2 \times 6 =$ _____

Review and Remember

Add or subtract.

$$\begin{array}{r} 43 \\ +77 \\ \hline \end{array} \qquad \begin{array}{r} 231 \\ -107 \\ \hline \end{array} \qquad \begin{array}{r} 211 \\ +563 \\ \hline \end{array} \qquad \begin{array}{r} 430 \\ -179 \\ \hline \end{array} \qquad \begin{array}{r} 567 \\ +258 \\ \hline \end{array}$$

Use after Grade 2, text page 350.   **57**

Name _____

Multiplying Across and Down

Multiply across and down.

Write the numbers.

1.

$\underline{2} \times \underline{3} = \underline{6}$ $\begin{array}{r} 3 \\ \times 2 \\ \hline 6 \end{array}$

2.

$\times \underline{}$

$\underline{} \times \underline{} = \underline{}$

3.

$\times \underline{}$

$\underline{} \times \underline{} = \underline{}$

Review and Remember

Circle the best estimate.

Milk in a baby's bottle:	1 gallon	1 pint
The weight of a large book:	1 gram	1 kilogram
The weight of a watermelon:	more than 1 pound	less than 1 pound
Temperature of ice:	0°C	30°C

Multiplying in Any Order

Find each product.

1.
$$\begin{array}{r} 3 \\ \times 5 \\ \hline 15 \end{array} \qquad \begin{array}{r} 5 \\ \times 3 \\ \hline \end{array}$$

2.
$$\begin{array}{r} 2 \\ \times 6 \\ \hline \end{array} \qquad \begin{array}{r} 6 \\ \times 2 \\ \hline \end{array}$$

3.
$$\begin{array}{r} 4 \\ \times 5 \\ \hline \end{array} \qquad \begin{array}{r} 5 \\ \times 4 \\ \hline \end{array}$$

4.
$$\begin{array}{r} 6 \\ \times 1 \\ \hline \end{array} \qquad \begin{array}{r} 1 \\ \times 6 \\ \hline \end{array}$$

5. $2 \times 4 = \underline{\hspace{1cm}}$

   $4 \times 2 = \underline{\hspace{1cm}}$

6. $2 \times 3 = \underline{\hspace{1cm}}$

   $3 \times 2 = \underline{\hspace{1cm}}$

7. $2 \times 1 = \underline{\hspace{1cm}}$

   $1 \times 2 = \underline{\hspace{1cm}}$

8. $2 \times 5 = \underline{\hspace{1cm}}$

   $5 \times 2 = \underline{\hspace{1cm}}$

Review and Remember

Write each time.

_____   _____   _____

Name _____

Exploring Division

Circle equal groups.

Write the number in each group.

1. ○ ○ ○   2 groups of ___   2. ○ ○ ○ ○ 2 groups of ___
   ○ ○ ○   ○ ○ ○ ○

3. ○ ○ ○ ○ 4 groups of ___   4. ○ ○ ○   5 groups of ___
   ○ ○ ○ ○   ○ ○ ○
   ○ ○ ○ ○   ○ ○ ○
   ○ ○ ○ ○   ○ ○ ○
                                  ○ ○ ○

5. ○ ○ ○ ○ 5 groups of ___   6. ○ ○ ○ ○ ○ 5 groups of ___
   ○ ○ ○ ○   ○ ○ ○ ○ ○
   ○ ○ ○ ○   ○ ○ ○ ○ ○
   ○ ○ ○ ○   ○ ○ ○ ○ ○
   ○ ○ ○ ○   ○ ○ ○ ○ ○

Review and Remember

Add or subtract.

$$
\begin{array}{r} 18 \\ + 9 \\ \hline \end{array}
\qquad
\begin{array}{r} 72 \\ - 5 \\ \hline \end{array}
\qquad
\begin{array}{r} 87 \\ - 4 \\ \hline \end{array}
\qquad
\begin{array}{r} 29 \\ +63 \\ \hline \end{array}
\qquad
\begin{array}{r} 45 \\ +468 \\ \hline \end{array}
$$